DAILY KNITTING AGENDA

Date: _____

TO DO:
- _____
- _____
- _____
- _____
- _____
- _____
- _____

KNITTING PRIORITIES:
_____
_____
_____

KNITTING QUOTE OF THE DAY:

KNITTING TAKS OF THE DAY

NOTES

DAILY KNITTING AGENDA

Date:

TO DO:

-
-
-
-
-

KNITTING PRIORITIES:

KNITTING QUOTE OF THE DAY:

KNITTING TAKS OF THE DAY

NOTES

DAILY KNITTING AGENDA

Date: _____

TO DO:
- ☐ _____
- ☐ _____
- ☐ _____
- ☐ _____
- ☐ _____
- ☐ _____
- ☐ _____

KNITTING PRIORITIES:
_____
_____
_____
_____

KNITTING QUOTE OF THE DAY:

KNITTING TAKS OF THE DAY

NOTES

DAILY KNITTING AGENDA

Date: _____

TO DO:

- _____
- _____
- _____
- _____
- _____
- _____
- _____

KNITTING PRIORITIES:

KNITTING QUOTE OF THE DAY:

KNITTING TAKS OF THE DAY

NOTES

DAILY KNITTING AGENDA

Date:

TO DO:

- ☐ _____
- ☐ _____
- ☐ _____
- ☐ _____
- ☐ _____
- ☐ _____

KNITTING PRIORITIES:

KNITTING QUOTE OF THE DAY:

KNITTING TAKS OF THE DAY

NOTES

DAILY KNITTING AGENDA

Date:

TO DO:

KNITTING PRIORITIES:

KNITTING QUOTE OF THE DAY:

KNITTING TAKS OF THE DAY

NOTES

DAILY KNITTING AGENDA

Date: _____

TO DO:

- [ ] _____
- [ ] _____
- [ ] _____
- [ ] _____
- [ ] _____
- [ ] _____
- [ ] _____

KNITTING PRIORITIES:

KNITTING QUOTE OF THE DAY:

KNITTING TAKS OF THE DAY

NOTES

DAILY KNITTING AGENDA

Date: _____

TO DO:

- _____
- _____
- _____
- _____
- _____
- _____
- _____

KNITTING PRIORITIES:

KNITTING QUOTE OF THE DAY:

KNITTING TAKS OF THE DAY

NOTES

DAILY KNITTING AGENDA

Date:

TO DO:

KNITTING PRIORITIES:

KNITTING QUOTE OF THE DAY:

KNITTING TAKS OF THE DAY

NOTES

DAILY KNITTING AGENDA

Date:

TO DO:

KNITTING PRIORITIES:

KNITTING QUOTE OF THE DAY:

KNITTING TAKS OF THE DAY

NOTES

DAILY KNITTING AGENDA

Date: _____

TO DO:

KNITTING PRIORITIES:

KNITTING QUOTE OF THE DAY:

KNITTING TAKS OF THE DAY

NOTES

DAILY KNITTING AGENDA

Date:

TO DO:

-
-
-
-
-

KNITTING PRIORITIES:

KNITTING QUOTE OF THE DAY:

KNITTING TAKS OF THE DAY

NOTES

DAILY KNITTING AGENDA

Date:

TO DO:

KNITTING PRIORITIES:

KNITTING QUOTE OF THE DAY:

KNITTING TAKS OF THE DAY

NOTES

DAILY KNITTING AGENDA

Date:

TO DO:

KNITTING PRIORITIES:

KNITTING QUOTE OF THE DAY:

KNITTING TAKS OF THE DAY

NOTES

DAILY KNITTING AGENDA

Date: _____

TO DO:
- ☐ _____
- ☐ _____
- ☐ _____
- ☐ _____
- ☐ _____
- ☐ _____
- ☐ _____

KNITTING PRIORITIES:
_____
_____
_____

KNITTING QUOTE OF THE DAY:
_____
_____

KNITTING TAKS OF THE DAY
_____

NOTES
_____

DAILY KNITTING AGENDA

TO DO:

KNITTING PRIORITIES:

KNITTING QUOTE OF THE DAY:

KNITTING TAKS OF THE DAY

NOTES

DAILY KNITTING AGENDA

Date:

TO DO:
- [ ]
- [ ]
- [ ]
- [ ]
- [ ]
- [ ]
- [ ]
- [ ]

KNITTING PRIORITIES:

KNITTING QUOTE OF THE DAY:

KNITTING TAKS OF THE DAY

NOTES

DAILY KNITTING AGENDA

Date:

TO DO:

KNITTING PRIORITIES:

KNITTING QUOTE OF THE DAY:

KNITTING TAKS OF THE DAY

NOTES

DAILY KNITTING AGENDA

Date: _____

TO DO:

KNITTING PRIORITIES:

KNITTING QUOTE OF THE DAY:

KNITTING TAKS OF THE DAY

NOTES

DAILY KNITTING AGENDA

Date:

TO DO:

KNITTING PRIORITIES:

KNITTING QUOTE OF THE DAY:

KNITTING TAKS OF THE DAY

NOTES

DAILY KNITTING AGENDA

Date:

TO DO:

KNITTING PRIORITIES:

KNITTING QUOTE OF THE DAY:

KNITTING TAKS OF THE DAY

NOTES

DAILY KNITTING AGENDA

Date:

TO DO:

KNITTING PRIORITIES:

KNITTING QUOTE OF THE DAY:

KNITTING TAKS OF THE DAY

NOTES

DAILY KNITTING AGENDA

Date:

TO DO:

KNITTING PRIORITIES:

KNITTING QUOTE OF THE DAY:

KNITTING TAKS OF THE DAY

NOTES

DAILY KNITTING AGENDA

TO DO:

-
-
-
-
-
-

KNITTING PRIORITIES:

KNITTING QUOTE OF THE DAY:

KNITTING TAKS OF THE DAY

NOTES

DAILY KNITTING AGENDA

Date:

TO DO:

KNITTING PRIORITIES:

KNITTING QUOTE OF THE DAY:

KNITTING TAKS OF THE DAY

NOTES

DAILY KNITTING AGENDA

Date:

TO DO:

KNITTING PRIORITIES:

KNITTING QUOTE OF THE DAY:

KNITTING TAKS OF THE DAY

NOTES

DAILY KNITTING AGENDA

Date: _____

TO DO:

KNITTING PRIORITIES:

KNITTING QUOTE OF THE DAY:

KNITTING TAKS OF THE DAY

NOTES

DAILY KNITTING AGENDA

Date:

TO DO:

KNITTING PRIORITIES:

KNITTING QUOTE OF THE DAY:

KNITTING TAKS OF THE DAY

NOTES

DAILY KNITTING AGENDA

Date:

TO DO:

KNITTING PRIORITIES:

KNITTING QUOTE OF THE DAY:

KNITTING TAKS OF THE DAY

NOTES

DAILY KNITTING AGENDA

Date:

TO DO:

KNITTING PRIORITIES:

KNITTING QUOTE OF THE DAY:

KNITTING TAKS OF THE DAY

NOTES

DAILY KNITTING AGENDA

Date:

TO DO:

KNITTING PRIORITIES:

KNITTING QUOTE OF THE DAY:

KNITTING TAKS OF THE DAY

NOTES

DAILY KNITTING AGENDA

TO DO:

KNITTING PRIORITIES:

KNITTING QUOTE OF THE DAY:

KNITTING TAKS OF THE DAY

NOTES

DAILY KNITTING AGENDA

Date: _____

TO DO:

KNITTING PRIORITIES:

KNITTING QUOTE OF THE DAY:

KNITTING TAKS OF THE DAY

NOTES

DAILY KNITTING AGENDA

Date:

TO DO:

KNITTING PRIORITIES:

KNITTING QUOTE OF THE DAY:

KNITTING TAKS OF THE DAY

NOTES

DAILY KNITTING AGENDA

Date: _____

TO DO:

- _____
- _____
- _____
- _____
- _____
- _____
- _____

KNITTING PRIORITIES:

KNITTING QUOTE OF THE DAY:

KNITTING TAKS OF THE DAY

NOTES

DAILY KNITTING AGENDA

Date:

TO DO:

KNITTING PRIORITIES:

KNITTING QUOTE OF THE DAY:

KNITTING TAKS OF THE DAY

NOTES

DAILY KNITTING AGENDA

Date: _____

TO DO:
- ☐ _____
- ☐ _____
- ☐ _____
- ☐ _____
- ☐ _____
- ☐ _____
- ☐ _____

KNITTING PRIORITIES:

KNITTING QUOTE OF THE DAY:

KNITTING TAKS OF THE DAY

NOTES

DAILY KNITTING AGENDA

Date:

TO DO:

KNITTING PRIORITIES:

KNITTING QUOTE OF THE DAY:

KNITTING TAKS OF THE DAY

NOTES

DAILY KNITTING AGENDA

Date: _____

TO DO:
- _____
- _____
- _____
- _____
- _____
- _____

KNITTING PRIORITIES:
_____
_____
_____
_____

KNITTING QUOTE OF THE DAY:
_____
_____

KNITTING TAKS OF THE DAY

NOTES

DAILY KNITTING AGENDA

Date:

TO DO:

☐
☐
☐
☐
☐

KNITTING PRIORITIES:

KNITTING QUOTE OF THE DAY:

KNITTING TAKS OF THE DAY

NOTES

DAILY KNITTING AGENDA

Date:

TO DO:

KNITTING PRIORITIES:

KNITTING QUOTE OF THE DAY:

KNITTING TAKS OF THE DAY

NOTES

DAILY KNITTING AGENDA

Date:

TO DO:

KNITTING PRIORITIES:

KNITTING QUOTE OF THE DAY:

KNITTING TAKS OF THE DAY

NOTES

DAILY KNITTING AGENDA

Date: _____

TO DO:

_____
_____
_____
_____
_____
_____

KNITTING PRIORITIES:

_____
_____
_____

KNITTING QUOTE OF THE DAY:

KNITTING TAKS OF THE DAY

NOTES

DAILY KNITTING AGENDA

Date: _____

TO DO:

- _____
- _____
- _____
- _____
- _____
- _____

KNITTING PRIORITIES:

KNITTING QUOTE OF THE DAY:

KNITTING TAKS OF THE DAY

NOTES

DAILY KNITTING AGENDA

Date:

TO DO:

KNITTING PRIORITIES:

KNITTING QUOTE OF THE DAY:

KNITTING TAKS OF THE DAY

NOTES

DAILY KNITTING AGENDA

Date:

TO DO:

KNITTING PRIORITIES:

KNITTING QUOTE OF THE DAY:

KNITTING TAKS OF THE DAY

NOTES

DAILY KNITTING AGENDA

Date:

TO DO:

KNITTING PRIORITIES:

KNITTING QUOTE OF THE DAY:

KNITTING TAKS OF THE DAY

NOTES

DAILY KNITTING AGENDA

Date

TO DO:

KNITTING PRIORITIES:

KNITTING QUOTE OF THE DAY:

KNITTING TAKS OF THE DAY

NOTES

DAILY KNITTING AGENDA

Date:

TO DO:

KNITTING PRIORITIES:

KNITTING QUOTE OF THE DAY:

KNITTING TAKS OF THE DAY

NOTES

DAILY KNITTING AGENDA

TO DO:

KNITTING PRIORITIES:

KNITTING QUOTE OF THE DAY:

KNITTING TAKS OF THE DAY

NOTES

DAILY KNITTING AGENDA

Date:

TO DO:

KNITTING PRIORITIES:

KNITTING QUOTE OF THE DAY:

KNITTING TAKS OF THE DAY

NOTES

DAILY KNITTING AGENDA

TO DO:

KNITTING PRIORITIES:

KNITTING QUOTE OF THE DAY:

KNITTING TAKS OF THE DAY

NOTES

DAILY KNITTING AGENDA

Date:

TO DO:

-
-
-
-
-
-
-

KNITTING PRIORITIES:

KNITTING QUOTE OF THE DAY:

KNITTING TAKS OF THE DAY

NOTES

DAILY KNITTING AGENDA

Date:

TO DO:

KNITTING PRIORITIES:

KNITTING QUOTE OF THE DAY:

KNITTING TAKS OF THE DAY

NOTES

DAILY KNITTING AGENDA

Date:

TO DO:

KNITTING PRIORITIES:

KNITTING QUOTE OF THE DAY:

KNITTING TAKS OF THE DAY

NOTES

DAILY KNITTING AGENDA

Date:

TO DO:

KNITTING PRIORITIES:

KNITTING QUOTE OF THE DAY:

KNITTING TAKS OF THE DAY

NOTES

DAILY KNITTING AGENDA

Date: _____

TO DO:
- _____
- _____
- _____
- _____
- _____
- _____
- _____

KNITTING PRIORITIES:
_____
_____
_____
_____

KNITTING QUOTE OF THE DAY:

KNITTING TAKS OF THE DAY

NOTES

DAILY KNITTING AGENDA

Date:

TO DO:

KNITTING PRIORITIES:

KNITTING QUOTE OF THE DAY:

KNITTING TAKS OF THE DAY

NOTES

DAILY KNITTING AGENDA

Date: _____

TO DO: KNITTING PRIORITIES:

☐ _____
☐ _____
☐ _____
☐ _____   KNITTING QUOTE OF THE DAY:
☐ _____
☐ _____
☐ _____

KNITTING TAKS OF THE DAY

NOTES

DAILY KNITTING AGENDA

Date:

TO DO:

KNITTING PRIORITIES:

KNITTING QUOTE OF THE DAY:

KNITTING TAKS OF THE DAY

NOTES

DAILY KNITTING AGENDA

Date:

TO DO:

KNITTING PRIORITIES:

KNITTING QUOTE OF THE DAY:

KNITTING TAKS OF THE DAY

NOTES

DAILY KNITTING AGENDA

Date:

TO DO:

KNITTING PRIORITIES:

KNITTING QUOTE OF THE DAY:

KNITTING TAKS OF THE DAY

NOTES

DAILY KNITTING AGENDA

Date:

TO DO:

KNITTING PRIORITIES:

KNITTING QUOTE OF THE DAY:

KNITTING TAKS OF THE DAY

NOTES

DAILY KNITTING AGENDA

TO DO:

KNITTING PRIORITIES:

KNITTING QUOTE OF THE DAY:

KNITTING TAKS OF THE DAY

NOTES

DAILY KNITTING AGENDA

Date: _____

TO DO:
- ☐ _____
- ☐ _____
- ☐ _____
- ☐ _____
- ☐ _____
- ☐ _____
- ☐ _____

KNITTING PRIORITIES:
_____
_____
_____
_____

KNITTING QUOTE OF THE DAY:

KNITTING TAKS OF THE DAY

NOTES

DAILY KNITTING AGENDA

Date

TO DO:

KNITTING PRIORITIES:

KNITTING QUOTE OF THE DAY:

KNITTING TAKS OF THE DAY

NOTES

DAILY KNITTING AGENDA

Date:

TO DO:

KNITTING PRIORITIES:

KNITTING QUOTE OF THE DAY:

KNITTING TAKS OF THE DAY

NOTES

DAILY KNITTING AGENDA

Date:

TO DO:

KNITTING PRIORITIES:

KNITTING QUOTE OF THE DAY:

KNITTING TAKS OF THE DAY

NOTES

DAILY KNITTING AGENDA

Date:

TO DO:

KNITTING PRIORITIES:

KNITTING QUOTE OF THE DAY:

KNITTING TAKS OF THE DAY

NOTES

DAILY KNITTING AGENDA

Date:

TO DO:

KNITTING PRIORITIES:

KNITTING QUOTE OF THE DAY:

KNITTING TAKS OF THE DAY

NOTES

DAILY KNITTING AGENDA

Date:

TO DO:

KNITTING PRIORITIES:

KNITTING QUOTE OF THE DAY:

KNITTING TAKS OF THE DAY

NOTES

DAILY KNITTING AGENDA

Date:

TO DO:

KNITTING PRIORITIES:

KNITTING QUOTE OF THE DAY:

KNITTING TAKS OF THE DAY

NOTES

DAILY KNITTING AGENDA

Date: _____

TO DO:
- ☐ _____
- ☐ _____
- ☐ _____
- ☐ _____
- ☐ _____
- ☐ _____

KNITTING PRIORITIES:

KNITTING QUOTE OF THE DAY:

KNITTING TAKS OF THE DAY

NOTES

DAILY KNITTING AGENDA

Date:

TO DO:

KNITTING PRIORITIES:

KNITTING QUOTE OF THE DAY:

KNITTING TAKS OF THE DAY

NOTES

DAILY KNITTING AGENDA

Date: _____

TO DO:

KNITTING PRIORITIES:

KNITTING QUOTE OF THE DAY:

KNITTING TAKS OF THE DAY

NOTES

DAILY KNITTING AGENDA

Date:

TO DO:

KNITTING PRIORITIES:

KNITTING QUOTE OF THE DAY:

KNITTING TAKS OF THE DAY

NOTES

DAILY KNITTING AGENDA

Date:

TO DO:

KNITTING PRIORITIES:

KNITTING QUOTE OF THE DAY:

KNITTING TAKS OF THE DAY

NOTES

DAILY KNITTING AGENDA

Date:

TO DO:

KNITTING PRIORITIES:

KNITTING QUOTE OF THE DAY:

KNITTING TAKS OF THE DAY

NOTES

DAILY KNITTING AGENDA

Date: _____

TO DO:

- [ ] _____
- [ ] _____
- [ ] _____
- [ ] _____
- [ ] _____
- [ ] _____

KNITTING PRIORITIES:

_____
_____
_____

KNITTING QUOTE OF THE DAY:

KNITTING TAKS OF THE DAY

NOTES

DAILY KNITTING AGENDA

Date:

TO DO:

- [ ]
- [ ]
- [ ]
- [ ]
- [ ]

KNITTING PRIORITIES:

KNITTING QUOTE OF THE DAY:

KNITTING TAKS OF THE DAY

NOTES

DAILY KNITTING AGENDA

Date:

TO DO:

KNITTING PRIORITIES:

KNITTING QUOTE OF THE DAY:

KNITTING TAKS OF THE DAY

NOTES

DAILY KNITTING AGENDA

Date: _____

TO DO:

KNITTING PRIORITIES:

KNITTING QUOTE OF THE DAY:

KNITTING TAKS OF THE DAY

NOTES

DAILY KNITTING AGENDA

Date: _____

TO DO:

_____
_____
_____
_____
_____

KNITTING PRIORITIES:

_____
_____
_____

KNITTING QUOTE OF THE DAY:

KNITTING TAKS OF THE DAY

NOTES

DAILY KNITTING AGENDA

Date:

TO DO:

KNITTING PRIORITIES:

KNITTING QUOTE OF THE DAY:

KNITTING TAKS OF THE DAY

NOTES

DAILY KNITTING AGENDA

Date:

TO DO:

KNITTING PRIORITIES:

KNITTING QUOTE OF THE DAY:

KNITTING TAKS OF THE DAY

NOTES

DAILY KNITTING AGENDA

Date: _____

TO DO:

- ☐ _____
- ☐ _____
- ☐ _____
- ☐ _____
- ☐ _____
- ☐ _____
- ☐ _____

KNITTING PRIORITIES:

_____
_____
_____

KNITTING QUOTE OF THE DAY:

_____
_____

KNITTING TAKS OF THE DAY

_____

NOTES

_____

DAILY KNITTING AGENDA

Date: _____

TO DO:

- _____
- _____
- _____
- _____
- _____
- _____
- _____

KNITTING PRIORITIES:

_____
_____
_____
_____

KNITTING QUOTE OF THE DAY:

_____

KNITTING TAKS OF THE DAY

_____

NOTES

_____

DAILY KNITTING AGENDA

Date: _____

TO DO:

- [ ] _____
- [ ] _____
- [ ] _____
- [ ] _____
- [ ] _____

KNITTING PRIORITIES:

KNITTING QUOTE OF THE DAY:

KNITTING TAKS OF THE DAY

NOTES

DAILY KNITTING AGENDA

Date: _____

TO DO:
- ☐ _____
- ☐ _____
- ☐ _____
- ☐ _____
- ☐ _____
- ☐ _____
- ☐ _____

KNITTING PRIORITIES:

KNITTING QUOTE OF THE DAY:

KNITTING TAKS OF THE DAY

NOTES

DAILY KNITTING AGENDA

TO DO:

KNITTING PRIORITIES:

KNITTING QUOTE OF THE DAY:

KNITTING TAKS OF THE DAY

NOTES

DAILY KNITTING AGENDA

Date: _____

TO DO:

- _____
- _____
- _____
- _____
- _____
- _____
- _____

KNITTING PRIORITIES:

_____
_____
_____
_____

KNITTING QUOTE OF THE DAY:

KNITTING TAKS OF THE DAY

NOTES

DAILY KNITTING AGENDA

Date:

TO DO:

KNITTING PRIORITIES:

KNITTING QUOTE OF THE DAY:

KNITTING TAKS OF THE DAY

NOTES

DAILY KNITTING AGENDA

Date:

TO DO:

KNITTING PRIORITIES:

KNITTING QUOTE OF THE DAY:

KNITTING TAKS OF THE DAY

NOTES

DAILY KNITTING AGENDA

Date:

TO DO:

KNITTING PRIORITIES:

KNITTING QUOTE OF THE DAY:

KNITTING TAKS OF THE DAY

NOTES

DAILY KNITTING AGENDA

Date: _____

TO DO:

KNITTING PRIORITIES:

KNITTING QUOTE OF THE DAY:

KNITTING TAKS OF THE DAY

NOTES

DAILY KNITTING AGENDA

Date:

TO DO:

KNITTING PRIORITIES:

KNITTING QUOTE OF THE DAY:

KNITTING TAKS OF THE DAY

NOTES

DAILY KNITTING AGENDA

Date:

TO DO:

KNITTING PRIORITIES:

KNITTING QUOTE OF THE DAY:

KNITTING TAKS OF THE DAY

NOTES

DAILY KNITTING AGENDA

Date:

TO DO:

-
-
-
-
-
-

KNITTING PRIORITIES:

KNITTING QUOTE OF THE DAY:

KNITTING TAKS OF THE DAY

NOTES

DAILY KNITTING AGENDA

Date: _____

TO DO:

KNITTING PRIORITIES:

KNITTING QUOTE OF THE DAY:

KNITTING TAKS OF THE DAY

NOTES

DAILY KNITTING AGENDA

TO DO:

KNITTING PRIORITIES:

KNITTING QUOTE OF THE DAY:

KNITTING TAKS OF THE DAY

NOTES

DAILY KNITTING AGENDA

Date: _____

TO DO:
- ☐ _____
- ☐ _____
- ☐ _____
- ☐ _____
- ☐ _____
- ☐ _____
- ☐ _____
- ☐ _____

KNITTING PRIORITIES:
_____
_____
_____
_____

KNITTING QUOTE OF THE DAY:

KNITTING TAKS OF THE DAY

NOTES

DAILY KNITTING AGENDA

Date:

TO DO:

KNITTING PRIORITIES:

KNITTING QUOTE OF THE DAY:

KNITTING TAKS OF THE DAY

NOTES

DAILY KNITTING AGENDA

Date:

TO DO:

KNITTING PRIORITIES:

KNITTING QUOTE OF THE DAY:

KNITTING TAKS OF THE DAY

NOTES

DAILY KNITTING AGENDA

TO DO:

KNITTING PRIORITIES:

KNITTING QUOTE OF THE DAY:

KNITTING TAKS OF THE DAY

NOTES

DAILY KNITTING AGENDA

Date:

TO DO:

KNITTING PRIORITIES:

KNITTING QUOTE OF THE DAY:

KNITTING TAKS OF THE DAY

NOTES

DAILY KNITTING AGENDA

Date:

TO DO:

KNITTING PRIORITIES:

KNITTING QUOTE OF THE DAY:

KNITTING TAKS OF THE DAY

NOTES

DAILY KNITTING AGENDA

Date: _____

TO DO:

KNITTING PRIORITIES:

KNITTING QUOTE OF THE DAY:

KNITTING TAKS OF THE DAY

NOTES

DAILY KNITTING AGENDA

Date: _____

TO DO:

- [ ] _____
- [ ] _____
- [ ] _____
- [ ] _____
- [ ] _____
- [ ] _____
- [ ] _____

KNITTING PRIORITIES:

_____
_____
_____

KNITTING QUOTE OF THE DAY:

_____
_____
_____

KNITTING TAKS OF THE DAY

_____

NOTES

_____

DAILY KNITTING AGENDA

Date:

TO DO:

KNITTING PRIORITIES:

KNITTING QUOTE OF THE DAY:

KNITTING TAKS OF THE DAY

NOTES

DAILY KNITTING AGENDA

Date:

TO DO:

KNITTING PRIORITIES:

KNITTING QUOTE OF THE DAY:

KNITTING TAKS OF THE DAY

NOTES

DAILY KNITTING AGENDA

Date:

TO DO:

KNITTING PRIORITIES:

KNITTING QUOTE OF THE DAY:

KNITTING TAKS OF THE DAY

NOTES

DAILY KNITTING AGENDA

Date:

TO DO:

KNITTING PRIORITIES:

KNITTING QUOTE OF THE DAY:

KNITTING TAKS OF THE DAY

NOTES

DAILY KNITTING AGENDA

Date:

TO DO:

KNITTING PRIORITIES:

KNITTING QUOTE OF THE DAY:

KNITTING TAKS OF THE DAY

NOTES

DAILY KNITTING AGENDA

Date:

TO DO:

KNITTING PRIORITIES:

KNITTING QUOTE OF THE DAY:

KNITTING TAKS OF THE DAY

NOTES

DAILY KNITTING AGENDA

Date:

TO DO:

KNITTING PRIORITIES:

KNITTING QUOTE OF THE DAY:

KNITTING TAKS OF THE DAY

NOTES

DAILY KNITTING AGENDA

Date: _____

TO DO:

- _____
- _____
- _____
- ☐ _____
- ☐ _____
- ☐ _____
- ☐ _____
- ☐ _____

KNITTING PRIORITIES:

_____
_____
_____

KNITTING QUOTE OF THE DAY:

_____
_____
_____

KNITTING TAKS OF THE DAY

_____

NOTES

_____

DAILY KNITTING AGENDA

Date:

TO DO:
-
-
-
-
-
-
-
-

KNITTING PRIORITIES:

KNITTING QUOTE OF THE DAY:

KNITTING TAKS OF THE DAY

NOTES

DAILY KNITTING AGENDA

TO DO:

KNITTING PRIORITIES:

KNITTING QUOTE OF THE DAY:

KNITTING TAKS OF THE DAY

NOTES

DAILY KNITTING AGENDA

Date:

TO DO:

KNITTING PRIORITIES:

KNITTING QUOTE OF THE DAY:

KNITTING TAKS OF THE DAY

NOTES

DAILY KNITTING AGENDA

Date: _____

TO DO:
- ☐ _____
- ☐ _____
- ☐ _____
- ☐ _____
- ☐ _____
- ☐ _____
- ☐ _____

KNITTING PRIORITIES:

KNITTING QUOTE OF THE DAY:

KNITTING TAKS OF THE DAY

NOTES

www.ingramcontent.com/pod-product-compliance
Lightning Source LLC
LaVergne TN
LVHW060200080526
838202LV00052B/4177